# the grotesque

Ornamental Prints from the British Museum

The South Bank Centre 1995

Published on the occasion of the National Touring Exhibition
*The Grotesque: Ornamental Prints from the British Museum* at
The Whitworth Art Gallery, University of Manchester, and its UK tour

Exhibition organised by Andrew Patrizio, assisted by Fiona Griffith
Education material for the exhibition prepared by Helen Luckett

Unless stated otherwise: photographs © British Museum
Catalogue designed by Edwin Belchamber
Typeset by Wayzgoose
Printed by Amica Fine Art Print Ltd

Cover: Arent van Bolten, from *Monstrous Animals* (detail) 1630s

ISBN 1 85332 138 9

South Bank Centre publications may be obtained from: Art Publications,
The South Bank Centre, Royal Festival Hall, London SE1 8XX

*C*hristoph *Jamnitzer*
*from* Neuw Grottesken Buch *1610*
*(page 29)*

# The Art of Communication

BT makes communication possible across the length and breadth of the globe, across time and space.

Working as partners, National Touring Exhibitions and BT help to bring the highest quality art within the reach of communities throughout the UK.

National Touring Exhibitions and BT are striving to open new doors and enable even more people to experience art, thereby enhancing both verbal and visual communication.

NATIONAL TOURING Sponsored by
EXHIBITIONS BT
ORGANISED BY THE SOUTH BANK CENTRE
FOR THE ARTS COUNCIL OF ENGLAND

# Preface

The suggestion that National Touring Exhibitions organise a tour of grotesque prints came from Antony Griffiths, Keeper of Prints and Drawings at The British Museum. It has become, we are glad to say, the third in a series of collaborations between the two organisations – the first two exhibitions being *Europeans in Caricature* and *German Printmaking in the Age of Goethe*. This initiative enables gallery visitors across the United Kingdom to see first-hand some of the great works held for the nation by the Department of Prints and Drawings.

Grotesques have lain in relative obscurity for over 200 years, yet represent an aspect of art after 1500 that is too easily overlooked – that outside the fine art traditions, with whose high seriousness and austerity we are familiar, some artists and designers gave vent to humorous, brutal and bizarre imaginings through ornamental design. Whilst the informality and invention of grotesques spring from a darker aspect of post-Renaissance European psychology, we hope these prints might also find new life in the contemporary world. It is a world in which they seem to fit well.

We are extremely grateful to Antony Griffiths for his lucid introduction and informed commentaries on each of the suites, as we are to his colleagues in the Department of Prints and Drawings for their kind assistance at every stage of this project.

We should also like to offer special thanks to Philip Dodd, Editor of *Sight and Sound*, whose contribution to this publication bears erudite witness to how grotesques continue to have a hold on the contemporary world through art, literature and film.

Henry Meyric Hughes *Director of Exhibitions*
Andrew Patrizio *Exhibition Organiser*

*A* rent van Bolten

*from* Monstrous Animals *1630s*

*(page 27)*

# The Grotesque

*I*n modern everyday speech, the word *grotesque* is used of something that is bizarre, distorted or absurd. But historically this is only its secondary meaning. In its primary significance, it is a technical term that refers to a type of decorative ornament that was immensely fashionable throughout Europe between 1500 and 1800, but is now more or less forgotten.

The origins of the style lay in a type of painting used as wall decoration by the ancient Romans. In the High Renaissance, antiquarians discovered examples in Nero's Domus Aurea on the hillside overlooking the Colosseum in Rome. These rooms had survived for nearly 1,500 years beneath the foundation of a later building. They had never been filled with earth, and were therefore in extraordinarily good condition. These rooms, or grottoes, gave their name to this type of decoration, which the Italians call *grottesco*.

Typical grotesque panels contain an elaborate architectural framework supporting a mixture of animate and inanimate objects, often impossibly and illogically combined. Henry Peacham, in his book *Graphice* of 1602, described the grotesque as 'an unnatural or unorderly composition for delight's sake, of men, beasts, birds, fishes, flowers etc. without (as we say) Rime or Reason'. It was this fantastical element, contrasting as it did so strongly with the standard conception of Classical rationalism and order, that so appealed to the imagination of designers and artists that they produced their own variations on it for 300 years.

Their main vehicle was the ornamental print, normally etched or engraved. Such prints were made in sets or series of plates of the same size, and sold at low prices not so much to collectors but to fellow artists and artisans, who plundered them for ideas for their own work. Craftworkers rarely made literal copies but, rather, adapted and used them to stimulate their own imaginations.

The stylistic connections that can be detected between some of these designs may be explained by the excellent distribution system that enabled ornamental prints to circulate very quickly throughout Europe. What was new in Paris one year might be copied in Rome and Augsburg the next, and adapted by local artists for new purposes thereafter.

This exhibition shows selections from twenty-two different sets of prints made by artists from most countries of Europe, all drawn from the British Museum's collection. Many are architectural panels derived from the types seen in ancient Roman wall painting. The rest are masks, fantastical creatures, stick men and suchlike, which all spring from the same imaginative impulse, but sometimes stray far from any strict definition of grotesque. Designers imported figures from exotic cultures – Turkey, China, Africa – and exotic animals ranged from recognisable giraffes and elephants to impossible creatures of all kinds. The human figure, too, was transformed, and either reconstructed out of different elements or used in fantastic assemblages. The results show a wide variety of effects. In some, the figures fluidly metamorphose the one into the other; in others, different elements are put together in a jarring clash. There are also contrasts in the degree of bravura displayed by the designers – some approach the genre in a low-key, delicate way, whilst others are distinctly more strident and assertive in style.

During the nineteenth century the tradition of the ornamental print died, finished off by the new industrial methods of production. Industrial design produced patterns in their tens of thousands, and the one-off image by the individual craftworker no longer had such a prominent place. As the ornamental print died, so did many of the motifs that it had nourished, and so the great tradition of the grotesque fell into neglect. Individuals, however, continued to rediscover it at periodic intervals. In the late 1920s some of these prints – in particular the *Bizzarie* of Giovanni Battista Bracelli (page 31) – enjoyed a brief vogue. One of the first articles on Bracelli was written by Kenneth Clark, who concluded: 'If he must be compared with a modern painter it is with his fellow-countryman de Chirico, who, by arranging a set of bedroom furniture in a solitary lunar landscape, combines a similar effect of volume with a similar effect of incongruity – a similar conceit'[1].

The connection with Giorgio de Chirico is not accidental, as the Surrealists certainly knew Bracelli's work, and much later, in 1963, Tristan Tzara wrote an essay for a small book[2] which reproduced the *Bizzarie*. In it he compared Bracelli's assembled figures with the Surrealists' *cadavres exquis* (exquisite corpses), the drawing game in which four people create a figure blindly across four different parts of the body. Through Surrealism, grotesques have continued to exert their fascination on another generation of artists. And, such is their charm, they seem likely to go on doing so for many years to come.

Antony Griffiths


Notes

1. *Print Collectors' Quarterly*, 1929, vol. 16, p. 326

2. Tristan Tzara, 'Propos sur Braccelli', in A. Brieux (ed.) *Les Bizzarie*, Paris 1963

Giovanni Battista Bracelli
*from* Bizzarie di varie figure *(detail) 1624*
*(page 31)*

# Memories of the Future

*[the body] is like a sentence which incites us to disarticulate it, so that, through an endless series of anagrams, its true contents may be combined*

Hans Bellmer, Surrealist

*I*magine a creature sewn together from the parts of several human beings – legs from one person stitched to the trunk of another, the head and face patched with features taken from different faces. Imagine another creature, half lion and half human. Or a third who, as the story progresses, slowly transmutes from a young woman into a tiger. Taken from, respectively, Kenneth Branagh's film *Frankenstein*, the children's animation serial *Thundercats*, and Angela Carter's short story *The Tiger's Bride* (from her collection *Bloody Chambers*), such fantastical imaginings are now commonplace across contemporary culture – whether in films or comics, poster art or literature. Science fiction has allowed a twentieth-century audience to take for granted all kinds of fantastic imaginary worlds. Popular television programmes such as *Star Trek* have licensed us to recognise creatures and beings who are often mixtures of recognisable features, but not always in the places we have come to expect – and who seem the result of a playful intelligence.

Every new work makes us see the works that precede it in a fresh way and it is certainly the case that the prominence of such fantastical creatures in contemporary culture is one point of entry into the fascinating world of the grotesque, with its strange teasing images, often of composite bodies and heads.

Like our own contemporary images, the grotesque relishes the trans-mutability of the human body and head. Such works see the human form not as something settled and given, but as a place of playful fantasy that can be built and rebuilt according to order. At its most visible, between *c.*1500 and *c.*1800, the grotesque was a playful contribution to that revolutionary shift to the secular which explored the status of the human form rather than assuming it was the mirror image of God. Our playfulness is sanctioned not only by new computer technologies, which allow us to reconfigure the human form and, God-like, invent 'virtual' bodies, but also by genetics, which holds out the possibility (and terror) that we can create the bodies we desire.

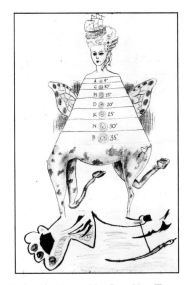

*Fig.1 Max Morise, Man Ray, Yves Tanguy,*
*Joan Miró,* Cadavre Exquis *(Exquisite Corpse) 1927- 28,*
*ink and pencil, Manou Pouderoux, Paris*
Man Ray © Man Ray Trust/ADAGP, Paris and DACS, London 1995;
Yves Tanguy © DACS 1995; Joan Miró © ADAGP, Paris and DACS, London 1995

If there is a point at which the parallels between the grotesque and contemporary images becomes a matter of influence, it is probably via Surrealism (fig. 1). Giovanni Battista Bracelli, the leading maker of the grotesque, was certainly known to the Surrealists and they in their turn have been an important source within contemporary culture. To look at the transmutations within the grotesque genre is to be reminded of the story about two Japanese bonzes that André Breton, one of Surrealism's key figures, liked to tell: '"Take a red dragonfly, pull off its wings and you have a pimento," one said; the other modified it to "Take a pimento; add wings and you have a red dragonfly"'.

Fig.2 *Yves Tanguy,*
Drawing *1953, pen and ink,*
*Private Collection, Paris*
© *DACS 1995*

Fig.3 *Giovanni Battista Bracelli,*
*from* Bizarrie di varie figure *1624*
*(page 31)*

Of course, the comparison between the Surrealists and the makers of the grotesque functions only in certain ways. While there may be connections between, say, works by Hans Bellmer or Yves Tanguy (fig. 2) and grotesques (fig. 3), the Surrealists worked within an established fine art tradition. In contrast, the makers of the grotesque freely adapted and even pirated the work of other makers.

In this sense, the makers of the grotesque may be more akin to contemporary comic book artists, set designers, animators and poster makers, whose work is often enjoyed outside consideration of its authorship. It is not simply that such work is body-obsessed, but that it can acknowledge freely the pleasures of ornamentation and fantasy, liberated as it is from the norms of the fine art tradition. For instance, Christoph Jamnitzer's extraordinary sexualised images (page 29) have something of the quality that the designer H. H. Giger gives to the female alien and her environment in the *Alien* series of films. And to look at the geometers of Bracelli in the light of our current imaginings is inevitably to make connections between his work and the robotic figures of cinema of the 1980s, such as those in James Cameron's *Terminator* and *Aliens* (fig. 4).

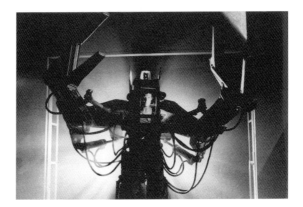

*Fig.4 Sigourney Weaver
in James Cameron's* Aliens

Someone who has worked across many contemporary popular forms is the film-maker Terry Gilliam, inventor of the composite animated bodies of *Monty Python's Flying Circus* (fig. 5), and director of a film adaptation of Lewis Carroll's fantastical *Jabberwocky* as well as *The Adventures of Baron Münchausen*. It is easy to see the connections between his inventions and those of the grotesque. In fact, it may well be that the impulses of the grotesque have migrated in part into what we have come to call children's culture. Look at toy-games such as *Citadel Miniatures* or the numerous computer games where the human figures and creatures scroll through fantastical architectural landscapes and it is there that can be found some of the descendants of the grotesque.

*Fig.5 Terry Gilliam, original*
*artwork for the film* The Life of Brian
© *the artist 1995*

There is one crucial difference, though, between the grotesque tradition and contemporary work. When Henry Peacham described the grotesque in 1602 as 'an unnatural or unorderly composition for delight's sake', working 'without Rime or Reason', he referred to nature and reason as norms with a confidence that we no longer possess. If our own contemporary grotesque seems darker than the original, it may be because we believe that science and technology might one day turn our imaginings about the body into fact. It is a troubling fantasy.

Philip Dodd

# Catalogue of Works

Note: references in square brackets are British Museum accession numbers.

# 1 Agostino Veneziano *(active Rome c.1516–36)*

## Six engravings of grotesques, *c.*1530/5

[B.XIV 565, 568, 570-1, 574-5; 1869-4-10-217, 221, 224, 226; 1873-8-9-770, 771]

The decorations in the grottoes of Rome were discovered in the late fifteenth century. Raphael and the artists of his circle adapted them on a vast scale for their wall paintings for Pope Leo X in the Loggia of the Vatican, between 1518 and 1519. With this famous covered patio overlooking the piazza in front of St Peter's, began the European vogue for grotesque decoration. No engravings were made at the time that directly copied sections of the Loggia, but Agostino Veneziano, an engraver working in Raphael's circle, made a set of twenty engravings in the early 1530s that drew on ideas he found in them and in classical grotesques. These six come from that set, which was reprinted throughout the sixteenth century.

 ## Jacques Androuet Ducerceau

*(active Paris 1549–84)*

**Twenty-six etchings of grotesques, 1550**

[2.AA★.a.13-1 to 26]

Ducerceau was one of the most productive architects and designers in Paris in the second half of the sixteenth century. These plates were first published in a set of fifty in 1550, and were copied and expanded to sixty-two by Ducerceau himself in 1562: this second set of plates was continually reprinted until the mid-eighteenth century. Ducerceau based his work on a set produced by the Italian, Enea Vico, in 1541, who had in turn adapted an anonymous set of twenty plates published in Rome in the 1530s. Ducerceau adapted some of Vico's plates, and added more of his own invention. In 1594, Ducerceau's plates were in turn copied by Johan Sibmacher in Nuremberg. Such a complicated sequence of adaptation or straightforward piracy is very common in the history of ornamental prints, which were produced before any international copyright law had been established.

The first plate carries a short message from Ducerceau to the reader in the international language of Latin: 'Behold there appears before you a second time our work on the ludicrous type of painting that mixes together various species of things (they call them vulgarly grotesques), newly increased and enriched with many plates. Farewell and flourish. Paris 1562'.

## 3 Jacques Androuet Ducerceau
*(active Paris 1549–84)*

### Four etchings of horizontal panels, 1566

[1850-5-27-256, 261; 1875-6-12-43, 41]

Besides the small vertical plates known as the *petits grotesques* shown on page 18, Ducerceau made another set of thirty-six much larger panels, the *grands grotesques*, of which four are shown here.

## Antonio Fantuzzi *(active Fontainebleau c.1537–50)*

**Two etchings of grotesque panels, *c.*1550**

[1850-5-27-132, 225]

In 1530, François I decided to refashion his palace at Fontainebleau (near Paris) in the most recent Italian fashion. To do this he imported a team of Italian artists and craftsmen under the direction of Rosso Fiorentino. Among them was the etcher of these plates, Antonio Fantuzzi, who is recorded in the accounts between 1537 and 1550. A document of 1550 states that he had made patterns of grotesque decoration for use by other painters, and among the 111 etchings that are known by him are some that reflect this expertise. Neither of these two prints (which, unusually, do not form part of any set) show any decoration surviving at Fontainebleau, and they may well be patterns devised by Fantuzzi himself, based on the ideas of Rosso.

# Juste de Juste *(active Fontainebleau)*

## Three etchings of monograms formed by human pyramids, 1540s

[I 7-101, 100, 98]

Seventeen prints are known by a single artist working at Fontainebleau. Twelve are of single figures; five show pyramids of male nudes. They have been tentatively connected with a certain Juste whose name is recorded in the Fontainebleau accounts, but this is very uncertain. The prints are of course not grotesques, but the distorted agitated figures derive from those that populate grotesque panels.

# Monogrammist IHS *(Italian)*

**Seven etchings from *Libro di varie mascare*, 1560**

[1875-7-10-1371 to 1376; 1868-6-12-370★]

Another type of print that is closely linked to grotesques is designs of fantastic heads. They are conventionally described as for masks, but were intended for adaptation in all fields of the applied arts. The first such set of eighteen plates was designed by Cornelis Floris (see page 25), engraved by Frans Huys and published in Antwerp in 1555. The whole set was copied in 1560 by an Italian, known only from his monogram IHS, in this series titled *Book of Varied Masks*.

# 7 Aloisio Giovannoli *(Rome c.1550–1618)*

**Eleven etchings of masks, 1610s**

[1932-2-17-37 to 43, 52 to 55]

Another series of thirty-eight masks was published in Rome in the early seventeenth century by Giovannoli, an obscure artist born in Città Castellana. His set also derives from Floris's designs of 1555, though with many variations and changes. This set was still being reprinted in 1781.

Veelderleÿ nieuwe inuentien van
antÿcksche sepultueren diemen
nou zeere ghebruÿckende is
met noch zeer fraeÿe gro=
tissen en Compertimenten zeer
beqwame voer beeltsniders an=
tÿcksniders schilders en alle
Cons tenaers ghedruckt bÿ mÿ
Ieronÿmus Cock:
1 5 5 7·

C·FLORIS INVENT·

LIBRO · SECVNDO·

Cum gratia et priuilegio·

# after Cornelis Floris *(Antwerp 1514–75)*
# by Jan or Lucas Duetecum

**Four engravings from *Veelderley niewe inventien*, book II, 1557**

[F 1-56; 1862-7-12-363, 365, 368]

The sculptor and architect Cornelis Floris was the most original ornament designer in the Netherlands in the sixteenth century. He was the prime creator of the Netherlandish strapwork design, which derives from patterns created at Fontainebleau by Rosso Fiorentino. Strapwork (seen here most clearly in the second plate) is characterised by broad bands set in three-dimensional space that serve as a framework for motifs of all kinds. As such, it is in essence a three-dimensional development of the traditional grotesque armature that presents a more two-dimensional effect.

The Dutch title of this series reads: 'Various new inventions of sepulchres in the antique style which are now very useful, together with very fine grotesque and compartments, most suited for engravers, carvers, painters and all artists, printed by me, Hieronymus Cock, 1557'. The first book, published the previous year, had contained twelve plates; this sequel contained sixteen, eight of which are of tombs.

# after Jan Vredeman de Vries *(Leeuwarden, The Hague 1526–1604)* by Jan or Lucas Duetecum

**Six etchings from *Grotesco in diversche manieren*, *c*.1565**

[1886-1-11-63 to 68]

Vredeman de Vries was the leading follower (though not pupil) of Cornelis Floris, and a prolific designer of ornamental prints in most of the styles and genres then fashionable. He worked most of his career in Antwerp, before emigrating in 1586. This series, with a title page and sixteen plates, was his chief exercise in designing grotesques, and shows the clear influence of the prints of Ducerceau as well as Floris.

Many grotesque prints have small cartouches in the centre. These are often fanciful, but sometimes allude to classical characters or legends. In this series the man on the horse leaping into the flames is Marcus Curtius.

# 10

## Arent van Bolten *(Zwolle 1573–before 1633)*

### Five engravings of monstrous animals, 1630s

[1972 U.979 to 983]

Arent van Bolten was a leading Dutch silversmith, who worked for a number of years in Rome. None of his silver work survives, and he is chiefly known for a large album of drawings of fantastic creatures, now in the British Museum, that was assembled in 1637. Some of these drawings were engraved in Paris in the 1630s for the publisher Pierre Firens. The set is very rare, and seems to consist of seven plates. These extraordinary animals derive as much from Hieronymus Bosch and medieval monsters as from the confections of the classical grotesque.

## 11   Lucas Kilian *(Augsburg 1579–1637)*

**Eight etchings from *Newes Gradesca Büchelin*, 1607**

[1870-5-14-2852 to 2859]

The grotesque spread to Germany in the second half of the sixteenth century. These eight prints come from a set of fourteen plates published in Augsburg. Kilian had spent the years 1601–4 in Venice, and this may have encouraged him to make these prints, which incorporate some plant-like tendrils from Turkish Moresque designs. Kilian's series was very successful, and no fewer than three sets of pirated copies are known.

# 12 Christoph Jamnitzer *(Nuremberg 1563–1618)*

## Ten etchings from *Neuw Grottesken Buch*, 1610

[1879-6-14-140, 141, 144 to 147, 156 to 159]

Christoph Jamnitzer was the grandson of the famous Nuremberg gold-smith Wenzel. This set, the *New Grotesque Book*, consists of three title pages, four pages of text and sixty plates. The dedication carries a pre-posterous (and doubtless tongue-in-cheek) comparison of the invention of these plates to Colombus's discovery of America, and another plate shows a 'Grotesque-tree' that bears the most bizarre fruit. The complete set is one of the masterpieces of ornamental design, and a high point in the history of grotesque. The British Museum possesses one of only four known copies of the complete book besides the loose plates shown here.

## 13    Matthias Merian *(Frankfurt 1593–1651)*

**Eleven engravings from a set of grotesques, 1616**

[1874-7-11-1826 to 1831, 1837 to 1839; 1873-7-12-114, 115]

Merian was a professional engraver, who spent most of his career in Frankfurt (where he trained the young Wenzel Hollar). He made this set, containing a title plate and sixteen plates, at the beginning of his career for a publisher in Augsburg. It was re-issued twice in the seventeenth century, and three sets of copies are known to exist. The last two plates on the second mount come from one of these.

# Giovanni Battista Bracelli *(active Florence, Rome and Naples 1624–49)*

## Thirty-two plates from *Bizzarie di varie figure*, 1624

[1910-3-24-5 to 16; 1928-12-14-2 to 21]

On the first plate of this famous series, Bracelli calls himself a Florentine painter, but we are still not certain who he was, and the only evidence for his career are the eighty-eight etchings he made between 1624 and 1649. Of these, by far the most extraordinary are the earliest, the set of fifty small plates he titled the *Bizzarie* and dedicated to one of the Medici family. Each plate consists of two paired figures constructed from elements of inanimate objects. In them the bizarre population of ornamental grotesques is detached from its setting and given an existence of its own. The set is very rare: only one survives complete, and this is one of eight other incomplete sets that are known.

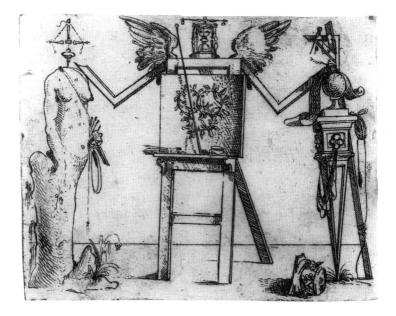

# 15

## after Nicasius Rousseel *(active London 1567–1640)*

**Ten engravings copied from *Seer aerdinge Grotissen*, 1623**

[1890-4-15-80 to 89]

Rousseel was a goldsmith born in Bruges who, in about 1567, moved to London where he remained for the rest of his life. He is now best known for his series *De Grotesco perutilis . . . liber*, a set of twelve plates engraved by Jan Barra and published in London in 1623; this is the earliest English set of grotesques. The original plates are rare, and the prints shown here come from a set of copies made for the Amsterdam publisher C. J. Visscher in 1644.

## Denis Boutemie *(active Paris 1620–58)*

### Twelve etchings of the twelve months, 1638

1861-7-13-1538 to 1549]

Boutemie held a position as royal goldsmith, and sources show that he was one of the most highly regarded virtuoso craftsmen of his day. But all his metalwork has been destroyed, and he was almost forgotten until his career was reconstructed from documents in 1992 . He is now only known from a few medals and various prints after his designs, of which this set is perhaps the best. The twelve figures, strictly speaking more like caricatures than grotesques, wear fantastic masque costumes, and represent the months (the titles were added underneath later): the second one, for example, represents the gluttony of Shrove Tuesday in February. The prints are documented as having been made as decorations for a folding map, but no copy of the map has yet been discovered.

### after Simon Vouet *(Paris 1590–1649)*
### by Michel Dorigny *(1617–65)*

**Three etchings from *Livre de diverses Grotesques*, 1647**

[1873-7-12-201, 204, 208]

Vouet was one of the most distinguished painters working in Paris in the first half of the seventeenth century, and held the position of *premier peintre du Roi*. In 1645 he designed and painted decorations in the grotesque style in the bathroom of the regent Anne of Austria in the Palais Royal (now destroyed). Like many of his works, he had them engraved by his son-in-law Dorigny, and these three plates come from the complete set of fifteen. Vouet stands at the head of French classicism, and it is notable how his logical mind has tidied up the anarchic grotesque into something more coherent and disciplined.

## Stefano della Bella *(Florence 1610–64)*

**Twelve etchings of *Ornament o Grottesche*, c.1653**

[1862-10-11-311 to 322]

Della Bella was a specialist etcher, who followed Jacques Callot as engraver to the Medici court in Florence. Between 1639 and 1649 he worked in Paris for French publishers. This set of twelve vertical panels, which falls into two subjects of six with two titles, was probably made after his return to Florence. Della Bella was a designer of genius, and some of his ornamental prints – notably his sets of cartouches – are among the masterpieces of the genre.

 **19**

## Wolfgang Hieronymus von Bömmel

*(active Nuremberg)*

**The set of six prints** *Neu-ersonnene Gold-Schmieds-Grillen,* **c.1695**

[1886-1-11-84 to 89]

Bömmel seems to have been a member of the large Bemmel family of goldsmiths that worked in Nuremberg in the second half of the seventeenth and in the eighteenth centuries. Now he is known only by two sets of ornamental prints, of which this is the first. The title translates as *Newly-invented goldsmiths' whims,* and the figures composed of twists of foliage add a new motif to the repertoire of grotesque.

 **20**

## Charles-Germain de Saint-Aubin *(Paris 1721–86)*

**Three etchings from** *Essay de Papilloneries humaines,* **late 1750s**

[1983-11-5-2 to 4]

Saint-Aubin was one of three famous artist brothers. He worked as a designer for fabrics and textiles, and held the position of *dessinateur du*

*Roi.* He made twenty-seven etchings, of which the best-known are two sets of six plates, one horizontal and one vertical in format, in which butterflies act as humans. Earlier designs show animals such as monkeys masquerading as humans, but this seems to be the only time that butterflies appear.

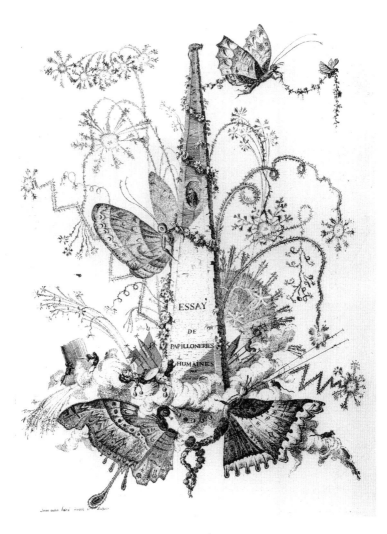

J. Pillement in.                    Anne allen S.

## 21 after Jean Pillement *(Lyons 1728–1808)* by Anne Allen

**Set of five colour etchings of *Nouvelle Suitte de cahiers arabesques chinois*, 1770s**

[1978-10-7-28 (1 to 5)]

Pillement was born in Lyons, the centre of the French textile industry. For the rest of his long and peripatetic career he worked primarily as a commercial designer, and his light rococo style never significantly changed. For some years between 1750 and 1762 he worked in London, where he apparently married Anne Allen. On their return to France, she made a number of small sets of decorative prints. These used a novel technique: two plates carrying different parts of the design were printed on top of each other to create each image. Both plates were inked in more than one colour. Some were of flowers, but a few show this charming adaptation of the traditional grotesque to the eighteenth-century fashion for subjects derived from China, or rather from their idea of what China ought to be like – the style called *chinoiserie*. The title states that they are 'for the use of designers and painters'.

## 22 Filippo Morghen *(Naples 1730–after 1777)*

**Two etchings, with added aquatint, from the**
*Voyage to the Moon*, c.1766/7

[1984-6-9-10, 11]

Filippo Morghen was a Neapolitan topographical engraver, now remembered only for his son Raphael, the most famous line-engraver of the early nineteenth century, and for this set of ten plates of which the title plate translates: 'Collection of the most notable things seen by Cavaliere Wild Skull and Sig. de la Hire on their famous voyage from the earth to the moon'. The set was dedicated to Sir William Hamilton, British Ambassador to Naples from 1764 onwards, and later a Trustee of the British Museum. How this fantastic series came to be made, and who designed it, remains unclear. Beneath the rococo *chinoiserie*, the old grotesque tradition can still be discerned.